Patron: Her Majesty The Queen
President: His Royal Highness The Prince of Wales

# The Associated Board
# of the Royal Schools of Music

Royal Academy of Music · Royal College of Music
Royal Northern College of Music
Royal Scottish Academy of Music and Drama

This is to certify that

**MAUREEN NAIRN**

*was examined in*
**Grade 3 Violin**
*and passed*
*in the summer term 2003*

*Presented for examination by*
MRS SUSAN B JARVIS

*Richard Morris*

R F M Morris
Chief Executive

**ASSOCIATED BOARD**
OF THE ROYAL SCHOOLS OF MUSIC

24 Portland Place  London  W1B 1LU · Registered charity No 292182

2003B/D125/833699/0/4/4/7/2003

# GRADE
# 3

The Syllabus of Examinations should be read for details of requirements, especially those for scales, aural tests and sight-reading. Attention should be paid to the Special Notices on the inside front cover, where warning is given of any changes.

The syllabus is obtainable from music retailers or from The Associated Board of the Royal Schools of Music, 24 Portland Place, London W1B 1LU (please send a stamped addressed C5 (162mm × 229mm) envelope).

In examination centres outside the UK, information and syllabuses may be obtained from the Local Representative.

# CONTENTS

*page*

Where appropriate, pieces in this volume have been checked with original source material and edited as necessary for instructional purposes. Fingering, phrasing, bowing, metronome marks and the editorial realization of ornaments (where given) are for guidance but are not comprehensive or obligatory.

**DO NOT PHOTOCOPY**
**© MUSIC**

**Alternative pieces for this grade**

Music origination by Jack Thompson.
Cover by Økvik Design.
Printed in England by Halstan & Co. Ltd, Amersham, Bucks.

A:1  2nd July

# Bourrée

## from *Water Music* Suite No. 1 in F, HWV 348

F major scale

Transcribed and edited by
Richard Jones

HANDEL

This Bourrée is the eighth movement from Handel's well-known *Water Music*, written for a royal party on the River Thames in July 1717. The original is scored for strings and continuo, with oboe doubling the first violin. Its boisterous character can be brought to life by emphasizing the upbeats to phrases and the repetitive rhythmic patterns. A fast bow stroke, on the string, will give stylish Baroque articulation. All dynamics and articulation marks are editorial suggestions only.

# Affettuoso

10ᵗʰ Sept.

A:2

## First movement from Sonatina No. 4 in G, TWV 41:G3

Edited by
Richard Jones

TELEMANN

Affettuoso (literally 'tender, affectionate') is a song-like piece that demands a *cantabile* style. The long notes in bars 3, 8 and 9 might start gently but grow more intense as they approach the following semiquavers. The trill in bar 2 might be played on the open string as is common practice in Baroque music. Dynamics are editorial suggestions only. Some slurs and ornaments have been added by analogy with the composer's.

Source: *Sei sonatine per violino e cembalo* (Amsterdam, 1724/5).

© 1998 by The Associated Board of the Royal Schools of Music

A:3

# Contredanse
## K. 269b, No. 1

Transcribed and edited by
Richard Jones

MOZART

This is the first of 12 contredanses, K.269b, written in Salzburg probably in early 1776. Their original instrumentation is not known, for the four that survive exist only in the form of an arrangement for keyboard. The contredanse is a lively dance movement in duple metre very popular in the late 18th century. Some articulation marks and bowing have been added by analogy with the composer's.

AB 2747

# MAKING THE GRADE · GRADE 3

**EASY POPULAR PIECES FOR YOUNG VIOLINISTS. SELECTED AND ARRANGED BY JERRY LANNING. EDITED BY MARJORY KING**

# VIOLIN PART

Exclusive Distributors:
Music Sales Limited
Newmarket Road, Bury St. Edmunds, Suffolk IP33 3YB.
This book © Copyright 1995 Chester Music.
ISBN 0-7119-5055-5
Order No. CH61087
Cover design and typesetting by Pemberton and Whitefoord.
Music engraved by Seton Music Graphics Ltd.
Printed in the United Kingdom by
Caligraving Limited, Thetford, Norfolk.

## Chester Music

(A division of Music Sales Limited)
8/9 Frith Street, London W1V 5TZ

# INTRODUCTION

This collection of 14 popular tunes has been carefully arranged and graded to provide attractive teaching repertoire for young violinists. The familiarity of the material will stimulate pupils' enthusiasm and encourage their practice.

The technical demands of the solo part increase progressively up to the standard of Associated Board Grade 3. The piano accompaniments are simple yet effective and should be within the range of most pianists.

Practical suggestions for fingering are given, but these may of course be adapted to suit the needs of the individual student. It is important always to feel a steady pulse, so that bow speeds can be planned appropriately.

# CONTENTS

# THE INCREDIBLE HULK (THEME FROM)

*Composed by Joe Harnell.*

This theme from the TV series is a wistful and attractive melody, which reflects the gentle side of the Hulk's nature, so bow very lightly through the slurs.

# YESTERDAY

*Words & Music by John Lennon & Paul McCartney.*

Most peoples' favourite Beatles song. Notice the F sharp and G sharp in the ascending
scale of A melodic minor (bar 4), followed by the F and G naturals in the descending scale.
The fingering relates to first and third positions, but if you feel daring try the whole piece in second position.

4

Oct 22d

# SUMMERTIME

*By George Gershwin, Ira Gershwin, DuBose & Dorothy Heyward.*

'Summertime' is probably Gershwin's most famous tune. The notes aren't difficult,
but be careful that you play the correct rhythm in bars 11 and 12.
Play the long notes with vibrato if possible.

# EL CONDOR PASA (IF I COULD)

*Musical Arrangement by J. Milchberg & D. Robles. English Lyric by Paul Simon.*

This is a traditional melody from South America, made popular by Simon and Garfunkel.

Keep a very steady tempo.

# YELLOW SUBMARINE

*Words & Music by John Lennon & Paul McCartney.*

This Beatles number needs to be played with a tight, accurate rhythm — don't slip into triplets in the chorus, and don't use too much bow. Notice that the verse is repeated an octave higher.

# BRIDGE OVER TROUBLED WATER

*Words & Music by Paul Simon.*

Here is Paul Simon's most enduring song.
Try for a full, rounded tone as the piece builds to a climax around bar 23.

# ITSY BITSY, TEENIE WEENIE, YELLOW POLKADOT BIKINI

*Words & Music by Lee Pockriss & Paul J. Vance.*

If you want to leave out the spoken sections, you can cut from the first beat of bar 10 to the second beat of bar 12, and cut bar 22 completely. Watch out for the $\frac{2}{4}$ bar.

# JEANIE WITH THE LIGHT BROWN HAIR

*Words & Music by Stephen Foster.*

This song needs really expressive playing.
Be particularly careful of the slurred ninth (A to B) in bar 14. The B should be really soft.
Don't grip the neck too tightly when you change position.

# I KNOW HIM SO WELL

*Words & Music by Benny Andersson, Tim Rice & Bjorn Ulvaeus.*

Many of the notes are slurred in pairs,

which should be practised carefully to ensure that the bow is shared equally between both quavers.

# ONE MOMENT IN TIME

*Words & Music by Albert Hammond & John Bettis.*

Make sure your bow speed is appropriate for the varying durations of each bow.

# BIRDIE SONG / BIRDIE DANCE

*Words & Music by Werner Thomas & Terry Rendall.*

Articulate the quavers in the first section clearly, playing off the string if you can.

If not, grip the string with little bows for a similar effect.

# HE AIN'T HEAVY HE'S MY BROTHER

*Words by Bob Russell. Music by Bobby Scott.*

Some of the rhythms are a bit tricky in this piece. If you have trouble with them,
practise each phrase slightly slower, counting in quavers. Be careful to count the rests in bar 21.

# AMERICA

*Music by Leonard Bernstein. Lyrics by Stephen Sondheim.*

In this lively number from 'West Side Story' the time signature alternates between $\frac{6}{8}$ and $\frac{3}{4}$ ;
you will need to keep this clearly in mind in bars 17 to 25.
In the latter section push the up bows before the accented notes.

# THE ENTERTAINER

*By Scott Joplin.*

This piano rag featured in the film 'The Sting'. Make sure you keep a very steady tempo.
You will find that the piece is quite a test of stamina.

9/99 (35304)

# Lullaby

## Op. 49 No. 4

B:1

Arranged by
Peter Kolman

BRAHMS

B:2

# In the Hall of the Mountain King

from *Peer Gynt*

2nd July

Arranged by
Edward Huws Jones

GRIEG

The repeat is not to be played in the examination, although it can be very effective in concert performances. You might begin **pp** and make the *crescendo* more gradual. You might also delay the *accelerando* until the ninth bar of the repeat. EHJ

# The Trout

### Theme from fourth movement of Piano Quintet, Op. 114, D. 667

**B:3**

Arranged by
Polly Waterfield

SCHUBERT

One of Schubert's best-loved songs, *The Trout* describes a fish swimming happily in a river before being caught by a fisherman. The composer later arranged the melody for the last movement of his piano quintet, nicknamed 'The Trout' Quintet, and this is the basis of the version here.  PW

10th Sept

C:1

# Blackberry Blossom

Arranged by
Edward Huws Jones

ANON.

This piece is in an American fiddle style known as bluegrass, which is a blend of old-time Appalachian folk music, blues and country music. It needs to be played fast but with steely accuracy! The double-stopped notes in the second half are optional. In bar 12 slide the fourth finger up to the high B.  EHJ

© Copyright 1997 by Boosey & Hawkes Music Publishers Ltd
Reproduced from *The American Fiddler* by permission. All enquiries for this piece apart from the examinations should be addressed to Boosey & Hawkes Music Publishers Ltd, 295 Regent Street, London W1B 2JH.

# Shepherd's Pipe

### No. 28 from *For Children*, Vol. II

Arranged by
Ede Zathureczky

BARTÓK

Inspired by his interest in the peasant music of Hungary and Slovakia, Béla Bartók (1881–1945) compiled *For Children* (1908–9), two volumes of Hungarian and Slovakian folk music adapted for the piano. The present arrangement is of a Slovakian folk tune.

# Lazy Time

TIMOTHY KRAEMER

This piece needs a laid-back but confidently rhythmic style. Listening to recordings of a great jazz violinist such as Stephane Grappelli will help you to enjoy the 'smeary' effect of the jazz slide in bars 7, 15 and 31.

© 1996 by Faber Music Ltd
Reproduced from *Gypsy Jazz* by permission. All enquiries for this piece apart from the examinations should be addressed to Faber Music Ltd, 3 Queen Square, London WC1N 3AU.

AB 2747

## Checklist of Scales and Arpeggios

Candidates and teachers may find this checklist useful in learning the requirements of the grade. Full details of the forms of the various requirements, including details of rhythms, starting notes and bowing patterns, are given in the syllabus and in the scale books published by the Board.

# Grade 3

| | | | separate bows | | | | | | slurred | | | | | |
|---|---|---|---|---|---|---|---|---|---|---|---|---|---|---|
| **Major Scales** | | | | | | | | | *two quavers to a bow* | | | | | |
| | E Major | 1 Octave | ✓ | | | | | | ✓ | | | | | |
| | G Major | 2 Octaves | ✓ | | | | | | ✓ | | | | | |
| | A Major | 2 Octaves | ✓ | | | | | | ✓ | | | | | |
| | B♭ Major | 2 Octaves | ✓ | | | | | | ✓ | | | | | |
| | D Major | 2 Octaves | ✓ | | | | | | ✓ | | | | | |
| **Minor Scales** (*melodic* or *harmonic*) | | | | | | | | | *two quavers to a bow* | | | | | |
| | E Minor | 1 Octave | ✓ | | | | | | ✓ | | | | | |
| | G Minor | 2 Octaves | ✓ | | | | | | ✓ | | | | | |
| | A Minor | 2 Octaves | ✓ | | | | | | ✓ | | | | | |
| | B♭ Minor | 2 Octaves | ✓ | | | | | | ✓ | | | | | |
| | D Minor | 2 Octaves | ✓ | | | | | | ✓ | | | | | |
| **Chromatic Scales** | | | | | | | | | *not applicable* | | | | | |
| | on G | 1 Octave | | | | | | | | | | | | |
| | on D | 1 Octave | | | | | | | | | | | | |
| | on A | 1 Octave | | | | | | | | | | | | |
| **Major Arpeggios** | | | | | | | | | *three notes to a bow* | | | | | |
| | E Major | 1 Octave | | | | | | | | | | | | |
| | G Major | 2 Octaves | | | | | | | | | | | | |
| | A Major | 2 Octaves | | | | | | | | | | | | |
| | B♭ Major | 2 Octaves | | | | | | | | | | | | |
| | D Major | 2 Octaves | | | | | | | | | | | | |
| **Minor Arpeggios** | | | | | | | | | *three notes to a bow* | | | | | |
| | E Minor | 1 Octave | | | | | | | | | | | | |
| | G Minor | 2 Octaves | | | | | | | | | | | | |
| | A Minor | 2 Octaves | | | | | | | | | | | | |
| | B♭ Minor | 2 Octaves | | | | | | | | | | | | |
| | D Minor | 2 Octaves | | | | | | | | | | | | |
| **Dominant Sevenths** | | | | | | | | | *not applicable* | | | | | |
| | in C | 1 Octave | ✓ | | | | | | | | | | | |
| | in G | 1 Octave | ✓ | | | | | | | | | | | |
| | in D | 1 Octave | ✓ | | | | | | | | | | | |

Printed by
Halstan & Co. Ltd., Amersham, Bucks.